Honey for Baby Bear

Story by Beverley Randell

Illustrated by Isabel Lowe

"I like honey," said Baby Bear.

Honey for me,

Honey for me,

Honey for breakfast

And honey for tea.

"Who makes honey?" said Baby Bear.

"Bees make honey," said Mother Bear.

"Bees make honey," said Baby Bear, "and I **like** honey."

He went into the big forest to look for bees.

"I can see some bees," he said. "Where are they going?"

The bees went into a tree.
Baby Bear looked in the tree.
"**Honey**!" he said.
"Honey for me!"

"The honey
is all gone.
I'm going home,"
said Baby Bear.

"Oh help!
Where am I?
I'm **lost**!"

9

"I'm lost," said Baby Bear.
"I'm lost,
  but I'm good at climbing.
  I will climb this big tree
  to see where I am."

Up he went.
"I can see the river," he said.

"I can see Father Bear!"
Baby Bear shouted and shouted,
and Father Bear looked up.
"**I'm lost**!" shouted Baby Bear.

"Stay where you are,"
said Father Bear.
"I will come and get you."

"Here I am," said Father Bear.
"Come with me.
 We will go home to Mother Bear.
 The forest is too big
 for baby bears."

"Yes," said Baby Bear.
"I got lost."

"But I had some honey!"